The
Christmas
Road

ISBN 0 7151 0440 3

Published for the General Synod Board of Education
by Church House Publishing 1986

Produced for Church House Publishing by BILL BRUCE STUDIOS, Saffron Walden.
Printed in England.

The Christmas Road

an Anthology

compiled by Pamela Egan

designed by Bill Bruce

Church House Publishing
Church House, Great Smith Street, London SW1P 3NZ

Contents

Foreword

The trouble with Christmas is that it is so soon over. After a build-up which began around October, you can feel very flat by the evening of Boxing Day. Those decorations which are firmly left up until Twelfth Night look left over and sad as business gets back to normal and shops start the January sales even before the New Year. Churches make plans for Lent; schools start work for the Easter term exams. The baby in the manger had a short airing – then, as Cecily Taylor puts it,

> 'we packed him in
> the trimmings' tin
> till Christmas time next year.'

And yet Christmas should be a beginning, not an end: a road, not a stopping-point. That road goes on all through our year, taking us through the meaning of Christ's coming, his life, his resurrection, his good news for us. If we journey down the Christmas road, we go with shepherds and kings to the stable, but do not leave the road. It takes us on, past many other Christmases between that first one in Bethlehem and the nineteen-hundred-and-eighty-whateverth celebration which we shall keep this year, and we see that although the ways of celebrating may change, the reason for the celebration never does. Even when we reach today's Christmas, our journey is not over, for the meaning of Christmas does not end. We must keep travelling on.

This is why our collection of readings and poems is called *The Christmas Road*. It is meant for all the family to enjoy. Many of the readings are from books written for children, but all have a point which adults, too, will appreciate. Here are authors like Alison Uttley, Laura Ingalls Wilder, John Rae, Alan Garner, Richmal Crompton, as well as G.K. Chesterton, Philip Larkin, Brian Wren, John Henry Newman and many others. We are sure that teachers and clergy will find plenty of unfamiliar and useful resource material here, but this book is also one to enjoy for its own sake.

On *The Christmas Road* you will set out in wintry weather; wait, with Mary, for the birth of her baby; explore the meaning of the first Christmas. You will encounter feasts and families from days gone by. When we reach 'Here and Now', the readings may make you look again at how and why we give presents, sing carols, act in the nativity play. Not all is sweetness and light; sometimes 'The Goodwill Runs Out', and there is unhappiness and hardship on 'The Dark Side of the Road'. But 'Where the Road Leads' is to the other side of Easter; 'nothing is altered, but hope changes everything' and we look forward joyfully to the rest of the journey.

Walk on, walk on . . .   *Pamela Egan*

Weather for the Road

LEGENDARY WINTER . . .

It was Christmas night in the Castle of the Forest Sauvage, and all around the castle the snow lay as it ought to lie. It hung heavily on the battlements, like extremely thick icing on a very good cake, and in a few convenient places it modestly turned itself into the clearest icicles of the greatest possible length. It hung on the boughs of the forest trees in rounded lumps, even better than apple-blossom, and occasionally slid off the roofs of the village when it saw a chance of falling upon some amusing character and giving pleasure to all . . .

There was skating on the moat, which roared all day with the gliding steel, while hot chestnuts and spiced mead were served on the bank to all and sundry. The owls hooted. The cooks put out all the crumbs they could for the small birds. The villagers brought out their red mufflers. Sir Ector's face shone redder even than these. And reddest of all shone the cottage fires all down the main street of an evening, while the winds howled outside and the old English wolves wandered about slavering in an appropriate manner, or sometimes peeping in at the keyholes with their blood-red eyes.

T.H. White
(from 'The Sword in the Stone')

ONLY SNOW

Outside, the sky was almost brown.
The clouds were hanging low.
Then all of a sudden it happened:
The air was full of snow.

The children rushed to the windows.
The teacher let them go,
Though she teased them for their foolishness.
After all, it was only snow.

It was only snow that was falling,
Only out of the sky,
Only on to the turning earth
Before the blink of an eye.

What else could it do from up there,
But fall in the usual way?
It was only *weather*, really.
What else could you say?

The teacher sat at her desk
Putting ticks in a little row,
While the children stared through steamy glass
At the only snow.

Allan Ahlberg

A PRAYER BEFORE CHRISTMAS IN A TOWN

Dark streets reflect warm and glowing lights.
Crowds of shoppers carry gaily-packed parcels.
There's a hint of frost in the air.
It's very exciting, noisy – and alive, alive, alive.
Long live Christmas, and the love of Christ.

Chris Herbert

A Time of Waiting

'BE IT UNTO ME . . .'

(The Virgin Mary says 'Yes' to the message that the power of God will give her a child who is to be God's own Son)

Let in the wind
Let in the rain
Let in the moors tonight.

The storm beats on my window-pane,
Night stands at my bed-foot,
Let in the fear,
Let in the pain,
Let in the trees that toss and groan,
Let in the north tonight.

Let in the nameless formless power
That beats on my door,
Let in the ice, let in the snow,
The banshee howling on the moor,
The bracken-bush on the bleak hillside,
Let in the dead tonight . . .

Fearful is my virgin heart
And frail my virgin form,
And must I then take pity on
The raging of the storm
That rose up from the great abyss
Before the earth was made,
That pours the stars in cataracts
And shakes this violent world?
Let in the fire,
Let in the power,
Let in the invading might.

Gentle must my fingers be
And pitiful my heart
Since I must bind in human form
A living power so great,
A living impulse wild and great
That cries about my house
With all the violence of desire
Desiring this my peace.

Pitiful my heart must hold
The lonely stars at rest,
Have pity on the raven's cry
The torrent and the eagle's wing
The icy waters of the tarn
And on the biting blast.

Let in the wound,
Let in the pain,
Let in your child tonight.

Kathleen Raine

ADVENT PRAYERS

Father, may this season of Advent renew our hope and the trust which we place in the future that you have prepared for us.
> May our hope be strong in the face of all that makes for despair, fear and unbelief:
>> the cruelties that people inflict on one another,
>> the questions that cannot be answered,
>> the uncertainty of our tomorrows.
> May our trust grow stronger, Father, as we celebrate the coming of Christ in glory,
>> when pain, suffering, parting and death will come to an end,
>> wars shall cease, hunger be no more,
>> and everyone live secure in your eternal love.

Forgive, Father, all within us that is unprepared for Christ's coming:
> our neglect of other people's need,
> our involvement in what is trivial and our indifference to what is of lasting importance in our lives,
> our idleness in prayer and our lack of attention to your word.
Make us ready for his coming that we may run to meet him with love, adoration and gratitude.

We pray for all who wait for Christ with longing, especially those who endure hardship and injustice.
We pray for –
> those who live under the shadow of tyranny who await the day when Christ will set them free;
> those whose bodies are weak with suffering who yearn for the Christ who will make them whole;
> those whose dreams have died who look for a Christ who will make possible what seems to be impossible;
> all who hunger and thirst for righteousness' sake.
Father, with the Church in every century we pray –
> Come, Lord, come.

Michael Walker

ADVENT CAROL

Sheep like stones
In silent fold,
Snow like ash
Settling cold.

Walk a world
Bereft as dream,
Birdless wood,
Standing stream.

Bethlehem:
The children whine;
Travellers
Wait in line.

Tired men ring
The courtyard fire,
Tethered mules
Crowd the byre.

Stumble through
The cattle-pens;
Overhead
Roosting hens.

Spread with bales
The reeking floor;
Birthing bed:
Sacks and straw.

Trim the lamp;
Bemused and numb,
Watch and wait:
Soon, a son.

Jenny Overton
(from 'The Thirteen Days of Christmas')

Coming to the Stable

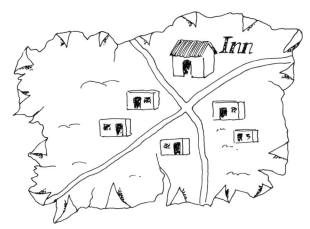

THE SAFETY OF THE WORLD

I saw a stable, low and very bare,
A little child in a manger,
The oxen knew him, had him in their care.
To men he was a stranger.
The safety of the world was lying there
And the world's danger.

Mary Coleridge

'O SIMPLICITAS'

An angel came to me
And I was unprepared
To be what God was using.
Mother I was to be.
A moment I despaired,
Thought briefly of refusing.
The angel knew I heard.
According to God's Word
I bowed to this strange choosing.

A palace should have been
The birthplace of a king
(I had no way of knowing).
We went to Bethlehem;
It was so strange a thing.
The wind was cold, and blowing,
My cloak was old, and thin.
They turned us from the inn;
The town was overflowing.

God's Word, a child so small,
Who still must learn to speak,
Lay in humiliation.
Joseph stood, strong and tall.
The beasts were warm and meek
And moved with hesitation.
The Child born in a stall?
I understood it: all.
Kings came in adoration.

Perhaps it was absurd:
The stable set apart,
The sleepy cattle lowing;
And the incarnate Word
Resting against my heart.
My joy was overflowing.
The shepherds came, adored
The folly of the Lord,
Wiser than all men's knowing.

Madeleine L'Engle
(from 'The Weather of the Heart')

LITTLE-BORN JESUS

When the baby borned
Joseph said to Mary
'What am I going to do about
This little-born Jesus baby Christ?
I never knew it was going to be like this
With all these angels and kings
And shepherds and stars and things.
It's got me worried, I can tell you
On Christmas Day in the morning.'

Mary said to Joseph
'Not to worry, my darling,
Dear old darling Joseph,
Everything's going to be all right,
Because the angel told me not to fear;
So just hold up the lamp
So I can see the dear, funny, sweet, little face
Of my darling little-born Jesus baby Christ.'

Joseph said to Mary,
'Behold the handyman of the Lord.'

Happy Christmas, Happy Christmas,
Christ is born today.

(This was sung by Lucy, aged four, to her doll and noted down by her mother.)

THE END OF A JOURNEY

(From a Nativity play written by Alan Garner for the children of his Cheshire village, and performed in the stables of the old village pub. The Three Wise Men, or Magi, arrive to find Mary and Joseph, with the Shepherds who have come to see the baby.)

(Enter Three Magi)

Joseph: Eh now, who are these?
            Lords and princes?
            Wizards? Sirs,
            This is a place for shepherds,
            Poor men, beasts.
            You'll get your gowns mucked up
            With slutch –

Mary: Let them come.
            And welcome, Sirs.
            You have been long
            On your long journey
            From your far country.
            But welcome. Though
            I know why you must bring
            These presents.
            Come. The Christ is here.
            Ask of him.

Joseph: Eh, what a pretty box!
            What's in it? Gold?
            Oh, Sirs, That's more than
            I can ever earn
            In all my years.
            You shouldn't have.

Mary: This gold is heavy, Joseph,
            For his head a crown
            To sit. King of this world
            He is, and Heaven's king.
            And heavy is the world.

Joseph: And this one, Sir?
            What's this?
            It's light. And smells
            So sweet –

Mary:

King of this world
He is, and Heaven's king,
And holy frankincense
They give to mark the
Priest, who takes
On him all cares.
And heavy are the cares.

Joseph:

This box is very nice,
But I don't like the smell.
Very kind I'm sure, Sir.
But I don't like the smell.
The smell, Sir, you see.
It's very good of you.
And the box is nice – good joinery.
The smell, Sir. It's not
Right for a baby. Of course
You weren't to know. Perhaps
We could change it–?

Mary:

Joseph.
King of this world
He is, and Heaven's king.
But he has come as man.
And man must die. And
We must bury him
With myrrh.
And heavy are the dead.

Third Shepherd:

I know it's hard to think on
When he's such a little lad,
But shepherds live with
Birth and death. You get
Used to it. Why, it could happen
Tomorrow, to any of us.
Death's not hard – for tups and ewes,
At any rate. Suns can set and rise:
When we go down, it's one long sleep . . .

Joseph:

Is he right, Mary?
I thought the angel said
It would all be different now,
When the lad came.

Mary:

Joseph, their sun must die and rise each year.
Our son must die once only:
And then for all, and rise
For all eternity.

Alan Garner
(from 'Holly from the Bongs')

JESUS AS GOD THE SON

(To understand why the birth of Jesus is so important, we have to realise that Christians believe he is not only a man who was born, lived and died two thousand years ago: he is also God. Dorothy L. Sayers tries to explain the difficult idea of God as Father, Son and Holy Spirit – the Three-in-One or Trinity – by saying that everything new which people make (a book, a painting, a cathedral, a machine) is threefold in the same way.

There is the Idea: without that the cathedral (or whatever) can't exist at all; with it, the builders may take hundreds of years, but they will always know that what they are working towards has been thought about and planned . . . and the Idea is like God the Father.

There is the Energy: a human being works in this world for what may be a short lifetime to put the Idea into a form which people can see . . . and that is like Jesus – God the Son.

There is the Power: the book or the cathedral that has been made is able to affect people who were not even born when it was first created; it can say things to them which may change their whole lives. That is like God the Holy Spirit).

Praise God that hath made man in his own image, a maker and craftsman like himself, a little mirror of his triune majesty.

For every work of creation is threefold, an earthly trinity to match the heavenly.

First: there is the Creative Idea; passionless, timeless, beholding the whole work complete at once, the end in the beginning; and this is the image of the Father.

Second: there is the Creative Energy, begotten of that Idea, working in time from the beginning to the end, with sweat and passion, being incarnate in the bonds of matter; and this is the image of the Word.

Third: there is the Creative Power, the meaning of the work and its response in the lively soul; and this is the image of the indwelling Spirit.

And these three are one, each equally in itself the whole work, whereof none can exist without the other; and this is the image of the Trinity.

Dorothy L. Sayers
(from 'The Zeal of Thy House')

THE HOUSE OF CHRISTMAS

There fared a mother driven forth,
Out of an inn to roam;
In the place where she was homeless
All men are at home.
The crazy stable close at hand,
With shaking timber and shifting sand,
Grew a stronger thing to abide and stand
Than the square stones of Rome.

For men are homesick in their homes,
And strangers under the sun,
And they lay their heads in a foreign land
Whenever the day is done.
Here we have battle and blazing eyes
And chance and honour and high surprise,
But our homes are under miraculous skies
Where the yule tale was begun.

A child in a foul stable,
Where the beasts feed and foam;
Only where he was homeless
Are you and I at home;

We have hands that fashion and heads that know,
But our hearts we lost – how long ago!
In a place no chart nor ship can show
Under the sky's dome.

This world is wild as an old wives' tale,
And strange the plain things are,
The earth is enough and the air is enough
For our wonder and our war;
But our rest is as far as the fire-drake swings
And our peace is put in impossible things
Where clashed and thundered unthinkable wings
Round an incredible star.

To an open house in the evening
Home shall all men come,
To an older place than Eden
And a taller town than Rome.
To the end of the way of the wandering star,
To the things that cannot be and that are,
To the place where God was homeless
And all men are at home.

G.K. Chesterton

THE NORTH SHIP: LEGEND

I saw three ships go sailing by,
Over the sea, the lifting sea,
And the wind rose in the morning sky,
And one was rigged for a long journey.

The first ship turned towards the west,
Over the sea, the running sea,
And by the wind was all possessed
And carried to a rich country.

The second turned towards the east,
Over the sea, the quaking sea,
And the wind hunted it like a beast
To anchor in captivity.

The third ship drove towards the north,
Over the sea, the darkening sea,
But no breath of wind came forth,
And the decks shone frostily.

The northern sky rose high and black
Over the proud unfruitful sea,
East and west the ships came back
Happily or unhappily:

But the third went wide and far
Into an unforgiving sea
Under a fire-spilling star,
And it was rigged for a long journey.

Philip Larkin

THE WORLD WAS IN DARKNESS

The world was in darkness
And nobody knew
The way to the Father
As you and I do.

They needed a light
That would show them the way;
And the great light shone
On Christmas Day.

Sr. Mary Oswin

THE LORD OF LIGHT

Your nativity, O Christ our God,
has shone upon the world with the light of knowledge:
for thereby they who adored the stars
through a star were taught to worship you,
the Sun of Righteousness, and to know you,
the Dayspring from on high.
O Lord, glory to you!

(from the Greek Orthodox Christmas Vigil Service)

HUSH YOU, MY BABY

Hush you, my baby,
the night wind is cold.
The lambs from the hillside
are safe in the fold.
Sleep with the starlight
and wake with the morn.
    the Lord of all glory
a baby is born.

Hush you, my baby,
the sky turns to gold;
the lambs on the hillside
are loose from the fold.
Fast fades the midnight
and new springs the morn,
    for the Lord of all glory
a Saviour is born.

Timothy Dudley-Smith

NONE TOO POOR

We are none of us too poor, or stupid, or lowly – it was the simple shepherds who saw him first. We are none of us too great, or learned or rich – it was the three wise kings who came next and offered gifts. We are none of us too young . . . or too old. There is only one thing against most of us: we are too proud.

Rita Snowden

THE BETHLEHEM STAR

Moonless darkness stands between.
Past, the Past no more be seen!
But the Bethlehem star may lead me
To the sight of him who freed me
From the self that I have been.
Make me pure, Lord: thou art holy;
Make me meek, Lord: thou wert lowly;
Now beginning, and alway:
Now begin, on Christmas day.

Gerard Manley Hopkins

25

Christmas Companions

THE WITNESSES

Magi in kingly splendour
Travelled from lands afar,
Slowly, with toil and labour,
They followed a distant star.

Angel-directed shepherds,
Filled with deep amaze,
Hastened from fold to stable
To kneel and worship and gaze.

But animals, humble and faithful,
Dwellers in byre and stall
Found their Lord in the morning
With never a journey at all.

Joyce Goldmanis

SPANISH CAROL

Shall I tell you who will come
    to Bethlehem on Christmas morn,
who will kneel them gently down
    before the Lord new-born?

One small fish from the river,
    with scales of red, red gold,
one wild bee from the heather,
    one grey lamb from the fold,
one ox from the high pasture,
    one black bull from the herd,
one goatling from the far hills,
    one white, white bird

And many children – God give them grace,
bringing tall candles to light Mary's face.

Ruth Sawyer

CAROL OF THE ANIMALS

The Christ Child lay in the ox's stall,
the stars shone great and the stars shone small,
but one bright star outshone them all.

The cattle stood in the cleanly straw,
and strange to them was the sight they saw.
The ox and the donkey watched with awe.

The shepherds ran from the uplands wide,
the sheepbells tinkled, the angels cried
– joy to the dreaming countryside . . .

The kings came last in a lordly throng.
The shepherds ran in the space of a song,
– but the beasts had been there all night long.
    Noel, Noel, Noel.

Sr. Maris Stella

CAROL FOR THE DOG

This is the carol for the dog
that long ago in Bethlehem
saw shepherds running towards the town
and followed them.

He trotted stiffly at their heels;
he sniffed the lambs that they were bringing;
he heard the herald angels sing,
yet did not know what they were singing . . .

But only being dog, he knew
– to follow when the Family led
to Egypt or to Nazareth.
And no one said

a word about the sharp-nosed dog
who stuck close to the Family then.
And yet, there must have been a dog.
This is a song for him. Amen.

Sr. Maris Stella

ROBIN'S ROUND

I am the proper
Bird for this season –
Not blessed St Turkey,
Born to be eaten.

I'm man's inedible
Permanent bird.
I dine in his garden,
My spoon is his spade.

I'm the true token
Of Christ the Child-King:
I nest in man's stable,
I eat at man's table,
Through all his dark winters
I sing.

U.A. Fanthorpe

Yesterdays

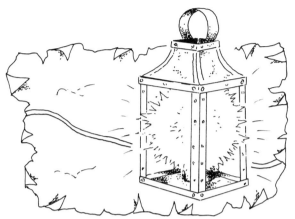

NO CHRISTMAS, BY ORDER: 1657

(During the rule of Oliver Cromwell, Church of England clergy were forbidden to hold services and for some years people were not allowed to celebrate Christmas in any way. John Evelyn, a well-to-do gentleman, was lucky to be let go after questioning; those not so fortunate were fined or imprisoned.)

December 25, 1657: I went with my wife and company to London to celebrate Christmas Day. Mr Gunning was preaching at Exeter Chapel on 7 Micah 2. Sermon ended. As he was giving us the Holy Sacrament, the chapel was surrounded with soldiers. All the communicants and assembly surprised and kept prisoner by them; some in the house, others carried away. It fell to my share to be confined to a room in the house . . . In the afternoon came Colonel Whaly, Goffe, and others from Whitehall, to examine us one by one. Some they committed to the Marshal, some to prison . . . When I came before them, they took my name and abode, examined me, why, contrary to an ordinance made that none should any longer observe the superstitious time of the Nativity (so esteemed by them) I durst offend.

John Evelyn
(from his Diary)

ELIZABETHAN MANOR-HOUSE CHRISTMAS

The great kitchen was decked with boughs of fir and scarlet-berried holly and many a bunch of bay. From a central hook in the beam hung a round bunch of holly and mistletoe intermingled with ribbons, and garlands swung in loops across the walls. 'The Kissing Bunch' Dame Cicely called the ball of berries and bade me beware of standing under it, for at Christmas everyone, young lords and all, would clip and kiss those maids they caught under its shadow. I noticed that Tabitha and Margery and Phoebe loitered much under the bunch that day.

Then Aunt Cicely pulled herself up from her chair and got to the baking, for spiced breads were wanted, and I filled the bread-oven with dry wood ready for her . . . There were chines and strings of hog's-puddings to go to the cottages and loaves of new bread for the widows and venison haunches for the goodmen at the farms . . . All the village would come to the manor on Christmas Day, to eat the roast beef and drink the mulled ale, and they would be asked to the hall to watch the Yule log burn and drink healths, the poorer sorts in the barley ale, the farmers in sack and canary wine . . .

There would be church in the morning, and then the great feast . . . Each year a wild boar was sent by the lord of Haddon, and from its flesh were made brawns and jellies, but the head and shoulders would be roasted in the kitchen and borne into the hall by the oldest man on the estate . . . Its head would be decked with a wreath of bay and rosemary. They would sing carols, and as the old man carried in the boar's head he would sing in his piping ancient voice:

'The boar's head in hand bear I,

Bedecked with bays and rosemary,

And I pray you, my masters all, be merry,'

and all would then join in with:

'Quot estis in convivio.' *(Latin for 'However many you are at the feast')*

Alison Uttley
(from 'A Traveller in Time')

THE ACCURSED THING

On the subject of all feasts of the Church my father held views of an almost
grotesque peculiarity. He looked upon each of them as worthless, but the
keeping of Christmas appeared to him as the most hateful, and nothing less
than an act of idolatry. 'The very word is Popish', he used to exclaim. 'Christ's
Mass!' pursing up his lips with the gesture of one who tastes assafoetida *(a very
strong spice)* by accident. Then he would adduce the antiquity of the so-called
feast, adapted from horrible heathen rites, and itself a soiled relic of the
abominable Yule-tide. He would denounce the horrors of Christmas until it
almost made me blush to look at a holly-berry.

On Christmas Day of this year 1857 our villa saw a very unusual sight.
My father had given strictest charge that no difference whatever was to be made
in our meals on that day; the dinner was to be neither more copious than usual
nor less so. He was obeyed, but the servants, secretly rebellious, made a small
plum-pudding for themselves. (I discovered afterwards, with pain, that Miss
Marks received a slice of it in her boudoir.)

Early in the afternoon, the maids – of whom we were now advanced to keeping
two – kindly remarked that 'the poor dear child ought to have a bit, anyhow,'
and wheedled me into the kitchen, where I ate a slice of plum-pudding. Shortly
I began to feel that pain inside which in my frail state was inevitable, and my
conscience smote me violently. At length I could bear my spiritual anguish no
longer, and bursting into the study I called out: 'Oh! Papa, Papa, I have eaten of
flesh offered to idols!'

It took me some time, between my sobs, to explain what had happened. Then
my Father sternly said: 'Where is the accursed thing?' I explained that as much
as was left of it was still on the kitchen table. He took me by the hand, and ran
with me into the midst of the startled servants, seized what remained of the
pudding, and with the plate in one hand and me still tight in the other, ran till
we reached the dust-heap, when he flung the idolatrous confectionery on to the
middle of the ashes, and then raked it deep down into the mass.
The suddenness, the violence, the velocity of this extraordinary act made an
impression on my memory which nothing will ever efface.

Edmund Gosse
(from 'Father and Son')

A LONDON CHRISTMAS IN THE 1870s

Nowadays it is difficult to realise that no Christmas preparations were made until the week before the day itself. All our excitement was packed into a short space. The boys were on holiday, and all over the place. Mother was mostly in the kitchen, presiding over mincemeat and puddings. I was set to clean currants, squeeze lemons and cut up candied peel. Barnholt *(the narrator's brother)* lent a hand at chopping the suet, but kept making raids on the lumps of sugar tucked away in the candied peel, which he assured me were very hard and nasty in the mincemeat, but had no ill effects on him . . .

Christmas Eve was the day we liked best. The morning was a frenzied rush for last rehearsals *(of the play the children were presenting for their parents and the servants in the evening)*, last posting of cards, last buying of presents. My father came home early, laden with parcels. The tea-table was resplendent with bon-bons *(crackers)*, sweets, and surprise cakes with icing on the top and threepenny-bits inside. The usual 'bread and butter first' rule was set aside, and we all ate and talked and laughed to our heart's content.

Then followed the solemn ascent to the study for the play . . . Personally I was thankful when this nerve-strain was over, and we all crowded down into the breakfast-parlour. Here, earlier in the day, mother and I had arranged the presents – a little pile for each, and we all fell upon them with delight. We were never fussed with a Christmas tree or stockings or make-believe about Santa Claus. Perhaps we were too hard-headed. Perhaps mother considered that waking up in the small hours to look at stockings was a bad beginning for an exciting day. As it was, we had a nice time before bed for peeping into our new books, and gloating over all the fresh treasures.

Christmas Day itself followed a regular ritual. Service at St Paul's *(to which the family always walked from their house in Canonbury)* . . . The post was the next excitement, and we displayed our cards on the mantelpiece. The traditional dinner of turkey and plum pudding and dessert *(fruit and nuts)* was followed by a comatose afternoon, during which Barnholt cooked chestnuts incessantly on the bars of the grate, tossing them to us as they were done.

Molly V. Hughes
(from 'A London Child of the 1870s')

TWO SIDES OF THE DAY

(The cathedral city of Ely in the 1870s)

All over the city men and women and children poured out of the chapels and churches exclaiming at the beauty of the day. It all looked as pretty as a picture, they said. The frost kept the sparkling snow from slipping away from roofs and chimney pots, but it was not too cold to spoil the sunshine. There was no wind. On their way home, whenever a distant view opened out, they could pause and enjoy it without having to shiver. The stretch of the snow-covered fen . . . was like the sea when it turns to silver under the dazzle of the sun. When they turned and looked up at the cathedral, its snow-covered towers seemed to rise to an immeasurable height. Then a wonderful fragrance assailed their nostrils. In steam-filled kitchens the windows had been opened now that the day was warming up. The turkeys and baked potatoes and plum puddings were also warming up and in another forty minutes would have reached the peak of their perfection. Abruptly Christmas Day swung over like a tossed coin. The silver and blue of bells and hymns and angels went down with a bang and was replaced by the red and gold of flaming plum puddings and candled trees. Everyone hurried home as quickly as they could.

Elizabeth Goudge
(from 'The Dean's Watch')

35

CHRISTMAS SIGHTS AND SOUNDS

(Susan Garland – who is really the author, Alison Uttley – lived on a farm in Derbyshire as a child, in the 1890s. Alison Uttley always wrote most vividly of the sights, sounds and smells of Christmas, perhaps because she remembered her childhood so clearly.)

A few days before Christmas Tom Garland and Dan took a bill-hook and knife and went into the woods to cut branches of scarlet-berried holly. They tied them together with ropes and dragged them down over the fields, to the barn. Tom cut a bough of mistletoe from the ancient hollow hawthorn which leaned over the wall by the orchard, and thick clumps of dark-berried ivy from the walls.

Indoors Mrs Garland and Susan and Becky polished and rubbed and cleaned the furniture and brasses, so that everything glowed and glittered. They decorated every room, from the kitchen where every lustre jug had its sprig in its mouth, every brass candlestick had its chaplet, every copper saucepan and preserving-pan had its wreath of shining berries and leaves, through the hall, which was a bower of green, to the two parlours which were festooned and hung with holly and boughs of fir . . .

On Christmas Eve fires blazed in the kitchen and parlour and even in the bedrooms . . . Margaret took the copper warming-pan filled with glowing cinders from the kitchen fire and rubbed it between the sheets of all the beds. Flames roared up the chimneys as Dan carried in the logs and Becky piled them on the blaze. The wind came back and tried to get in, howling at the key-holes, but all the shutters were cottered and the doors shut. The horses and mares stood in the stables, warm and happy, with nodding heads. The cows slept in the cow-houses, the sheep in the open sheds. Only Rover stood at the door of his kennel, staring up at the sky, howling to the dog in the moon, and then he, too, turned and lay down in the straw.

In the middle of the kitchen ceiling there hung the kissing-bunch, the best and brightest pieces of holly made in the shape of a large ball which dangled from the hook. Silver and gilt drops, crimson bells, blue grass trumpets, bright oranges and red polished apples, peeped and glittered through the glossy leaves . . . The lamp hung near and every little berry, every leaf, every pretty ball and apple had a tiny yellow flame reflected in its heart.

Alison Uttley
(from 'The Country Child)

THE CAROL SINGERS

(Christmas Eve on the Derbyshire farm where Susan Garland lived in the 1890s)

She hung up her stocking at the foot of the bed and fell asleep. But soon singing roused her, and she sat up, bewildered. Yes, it was the carol-singers . . .

Outside under the stars she could see the group of men and women with lanterns throwing beams across the paths and on to the stable door. One man stood apart beating time, another played a fiddle, and another had a flute. The rest sang in four parts the Christmas hymns, 'While Shepherds watched', 'Come all ye Faithful', and 'Hark, the herald angels sing.'

There was the star. Susan could see it twinkling and bright in the dark boughs with their white frosted layers, and there was the stable. She watched the faces half lit by the lanterns, top-coats pulled up to their necks. The music of the violin came thin and squeaky, like a singing icicle, blue and cold, but magic, and the flute was warm like the voices.

They stopped and waited a moment. Tom's deep voice came from the darkness. They trooped, chattering and puffing out their cheeks, and clapping their arms round their bodies, to the front door. They were going into the parlour for elderberry wine and their collection money. A bright light flickered across the snow as the door was flung wide open. Then a bang, and Susan went back to bed.

Christmas Eve was nearly over, but tomorrow was Christmas Day, the best day in all the year. She shut her eyes and fell asleep.

Alison Uttley
(from 'The Country Child')

Here and Now

WELLS CATHEDRAL
AT CHRISTMAS

The fluted stone of the cathedral glows
A gold ochre in the festive light
Of arc-lamps. It rises up into the night
Like a great force, with the squat pose
Of a rampart against the sky. It rose
Out of our documented past, the might
Of man's imagination hewn in delight
Of stone – its permanence, its weight, its poise.

We, the inhabitants, feature it as part
Of something all men celebrate, not
Merely a festival, our annual spending spree;
But something brilliant, undefined, like art,
Which gives us all the feeling that we sought:
The sense of both belonging and being free.

Michael O'Higgins

MOMENT OF TENSION

(At a service on Christmas Eve: nearly midnight)

It's three minutes to twelve and it's been announced; the tension, sweet anticipation, slowly begins to build. We slid into our places (those who did not sway in) quietly, hardly speaking, scarcely acknowledging our neighbours' existence, half an hour ago, and since then the moment that we are waiting for has dragged slowly nearer. Two minutes to go.

Outside the wind swirls round the corner, across the ice, through the resting pillar box, nipping at the nose of the drunk across the road, as hard as he has been nipping at his bottle. Inside it's well on the way but there's a minute to go. The purists glance at their watches: looks are exchanged.

The bell in the spire finds its voice, and the first chime of midnight rings over the town. Responding to the sound, the smiles begin to spread. The organist gathers himself and launches forth, the choir respond mightily, but both are drowned by the swell from the congregation:
'Yea, Lord, we greet thee,
Born this happy morning . . .'

Well-timed. The Vicar's done it again; the one verse that should never be sung on any other day has been the first verse sung on the new Christmas Day. Now the service may relax and follow its appointed course.

And at the end of the service greetings are joyfully exchanged, shouted, waved and, faces shining, we brave the cold walk home to coffee and a quick hour's sleep before the children wake, demanding their stockings. The church, now silent, settles to wait for the toy service in the morning, with its ancient timbers once more strengthened by that triumphant shout, that total affirmation of Christ with us now, and that most joyous of all Christmas greetings:
'O come, let us adore him, Christ the Lord.'

David Lankshear

CAROL SINGERS

'Away in a –' KNOCK! KNOCK!
'No crib for a –' RRRING!
You'd better come quick or
We'll actually sing.

'The stars in the bright sky
Look down –' on us now.
No baby could sleep
Through this terrible row.

'The cattle are lowing –'
And so too are we.
Don't hide in the back room:
You won't get off free.

'Bless all the dear children –'
Who sing at your door.
If you give us some money
We'll sing you no more.

Geoff Terry

THE BABY HAD A BIRTHDAY

The baby had a birthday –
we made the brandy sauce,
we drank his health
and spent our wealth
upon ourselves, of course.

We had a lovely party
and brightened up the place:
profusely strung
the tinsel hung –
you couldn't see his face.

Then when the feast was over
and we'd run out of cheer,
we packed him in
the trimmings' tin
till Christmas time next year.

Cecily Taylor

'. . . AND A PARTRIDGE IN A PEAR TREE'

(Prudence and James hope that their romantically-minded sister Annaple will decide to marry the rich young merchant Francis. They have hinted that she would like an imaginative Christmas present).

The parcel rustled. Annaple said, startled, 'Is it alive?' and moved back a step.

'Well, yes,' Francis said.

'Alive?'

'It won't bite,' Francis said reassuringly.

Annaple, still wary but too polite to hold back, reached for a trailing end of ribbon. She pulled cautiously. The ribbons fell away and the paper crumpled. Everyone gasped . . .

On the table stool a small tree in a red pot. A fat brown bird was blinking and clucking in the branches.

'It's a partridge,' Francis said, gazing hopefully at Annaple. 'And a pear-tree. Only a miniature pear-tree, of course, but they assured me it will flower . . .'

'Extraordinary,' said Papa. 'Quite extraordinary.'

He took a gulp of punch and stared at Francis as if he didn't believe what he was seeing. 'It's the cra– the most extraordinary present I ever saw.'

'But very original,' James said urgently . . .

Annaple didn't seem to hear. She bent forward to stroke the partridge. It made small pleased clucking sounds and sidled along the branch to nibble her fingers.

'It's delightful,' she said. 'It's the most delightful present anyone ever had.'

'She was pleased,' said Prudence as she opened the front door . . .

'She's a wonderful girl,' Francis said happily . . . 'Do you think she'd like another?'

'Another what?'

'Another partridge. In another pear-tree.'

'Another?'

'You see,' Francis said diffidently, 'I'm not used to buying one of anything – not just one at a time, I mean – you get out of the way of it when the trading ships come back with a thousand bales of silk, a thousand vats of wine, a thousand bushels of wheat. So actually I got a dozen. I always do, I didn't think –'

'What a wonderful way to be,' Prudence said. 'So you've got *eleven* more partridges at home?'

'Well, yes. And eleven pear-trees. I thought that perhaps I could send round one a day. And perhaps,' he said, 'some other little thing as well?'

Jenny Overton
(from 'The Thirteen Days of Christmas')

(You may be able to work out that eventually Annaple receives 364 presents, not all of which she wants. She does, rather surprisingly, marry Francis – with five gold rings, and thirty-five spares.)

THE HERDMANS AND THE NATIVITY PLAY

(The terrible Herdman children, 'the worst kids in the history of the world', have muscled their way into the Nativity play given by the children of a small American church and directed by the narrator's mother.)

Mother started to separate everyone into angels and shepherds and guests at the inn, but right away she ran into trouble.

'Who were the shepherds?' Leroy Herdman wanted to know. 'Where did they come from?'

Ollie Herdman didn't even know what a shepherd was . . . or, anyway, that's what he said.

'What was the inn?' Claude asked. 'What's an inn?'. . .

'What happened first?' Imogene hollered at my mother. 'Begin at the beginning!'. . .

Mother said she had better begin by reading the Christmas story from the Bible. This was a pain in the neck to most of us because we knew the whole thing backward and forward and never had to be told anything except who we were supposed to be, and where we were supposed to stand . . .

'What was that they laid the baby in?' Leroy said. 'That manger . . . is that like a bed? Why would they have a bed in the barn?'

'That's just the point,' Mother said. 'They *didn't* have a bed in the barn, so Mary and Joseph had to use whatever there was. What would you do if you had a new baby and no bed to put the baby in?'

'We put Gladys in a bureau drawer,' Imogene volunteered.

'Well, there you are,' Mother said, blinking a little. 'You didn't have a bed for Gladys so you had to use something else.'

'Oh, we had a bed,' Ralph said, 'only Ollie was still in it and he wouldn't get out. He didn't like Gladys.' He elbowed Ollie, 'Remember how you didn't like Gladys?'

I thought that was pretty smart of Ollie, not to like Gladys right off the bat.

'*Anyway*,' Mother said, 'Mary and Joseph used the manger. A manger is a large wooden feeding trough for animals.'

'What were the wadded-up clothes?' Claude wanted to know.

'The what?' Mother said.

'You read about it – "she wrapped him in wadded-up clothes".'

'*Swaddling* clothes,' Mother sighed. 'Long ago, people used to wrap their babies very tightly in big pieces of material, so they couldn't move around. It made the babies feel cosy and comfortable.'

I thought it probably just made the babies mad. Till then, I didn't know what swaddling clothes were either, and they sounded terrible, so I wasn't too surprised when Imogene got all excited about that.

'You mean they tied him up and put him in a feedbox?' she said. 'Where was the Child Welfare?'

The Child Welfare was always checking up on the Herdmans. I'll bet if the Child Welfare had ever found Gladys all tied up in a bureau drawer they would have done something about it . . .

When we got home my father wanted to hear all about it.

'Well,' Mother said, 'just suppose you had never heard the Christmas story, and didn't know anything about it, and then somebody told it to you. What would you think?'

My father looked at her for a minute and then he said, 'Well, I guess I would think it was pretty disgraceful that they couldn't find any room for a pregnant woman except in the stable.' . . .

'Exactly,' Mother said. 'It was perfectly disgraceful. And I never thought about it much. You hear all about the nice warm stable with all the animals breathing, and the sweet-smelling hay – but that doesn't change the fact that they put Mary in a barn.'

(The performance)

. . . We sang two verses of 'O Little Town of Bethlehem' while Mary and Joseph came in from a side door. Only they didn't come right away. So we hummed and hummed and hummed, which is boring and also very hard, and before long doesn't sound like any song at all – more like an old refrigerator . . .

I guess we would have gone on humming till we all turned blue, but we didn't have to. Ralph and Imogene were there all right, only for once they didn't come through the door pushing each other out of the way. They just stood there for a minute as if they weren't sure they were in the right place – because of the candles, I guess, and the church being full of people. They looked like the people you see on the six o'clock news – refugees, sent to wait in some strange ugly place, with all their boxes and sacks around them.

It suddenly occurred to me that this was just the way it must have been for the real Holy Family, stuck away in a barn by people who didn't much care what happened to them. They couldn't have been very neat and tidy either, but more like *this* Mary and Joseph (Imogene's veil was cockeyed as usual, and Ralph's hair stuck out all around his ears.) Imogene had the baby doll but she wasn't carrying it the way she was supposed to, cradled in her arms. She had it slung up over her shoulder, and before she put it in the manger she thumped it twice on the back.

I heard Alice gasp and she poked me. 'I don't think it's very nice to burp the baby Jesus,' she whispered, 'as if he had colic.' Then she poked me again. 'Do you suppose he could have colic?'

I said, 'I don't see why not,' and I didn't. He *could* have had colic, or been fussy, or hungry like any other baby. After all, that was the whole point of Jesus – that he didn't come down on a cloud like something out of 'Amazing Comics', but that he was born and lived . . . a real person.

Barbara Robinson
(from 'The Worst Kids in the World')

45

WILLIAM GIVES PRESENTS

William awoke and rubbed his eyes. It was Christmas Day – the day to which he had looked forward with mingled feelings for twelve months. It was a jolly day, of course – presents and turkey and staying up late. On the other hand, there were generally too many relations about, too much was often expected of one, the curious taste displayed by people who gave one presents often marred one's pleasure.

He leapt lightly out of bed and dressed. Then he began to arrange his own gifts for his family. For his father he had bought a bottle of highly-coloured sweets, for his elder brother Robert (aged 19) he had expended a vast sum of money on a copy of 'The Pirate of the Bloody Hand'. These gifts had cost him much thought. The knowledge that his father never touched sweets, and that Robert professed scorn of pirate stories, had led him to hope that the recipients of his gifts would make no objection to the unobtrusive theft of them by their recent donor in the course of the next few days. For his grown-up sister Ethel he had bought a box of coloured chalks. That also might come in useful later. Funds had now been running low, but for his mother he had bought a small cream jug which, after fierce bargaining, the man had let him have at half-price because it was cracked.

Singing 'Christians, Awake!' at the top of his voice, he went along the landing, putting his gifts outside the doors of his family, and pausing to yell, 'Happy Christmas' as he did so. From within he was greeted in each case by muffled groans.

He went downstairs into the hall, still singing. It was earlier than he thought - just five o'clock.

Richmal Crompton
(from 'More William')

JIMMY GIVES PRESENTS TOO

(William finds his four-year-old cousin Jimmy sitting gloomily in the hall on Christmas morning)

'They've gotten out,' said Jimmy sadly. 'I got 'em for presents yesterday, an' they've gotten out. I've been feeling for 'em in the dark, but I can't find 'em.'

'What?' said William.

'Snails. Great big suge ones wiv great big suge shells. I put 'em in a tin for presents an' they've gotten out an' I've gotten no presents for nobody.'

He relapsed into despondency.

William surveyed the hall.

'They've got out right enough!' he said sternly. 'They've got out right *enough*. Jus' look at our hall! Jus' look at our clothes! They've got out *right* enough.'

Innumerable slimy iridescent trails wound over hats, and coats, and umbrellas, and wallpaper.

'Huh!' grunted William, who was apt to overwork his phrases. 'They got *out* right enough.'

(After cleaning up the mess – and flooding the hall – William goes to breakfast.)

William entered the dining-room morosely. Jimmy's sister Barbara – a small bundle of curls and white frills – was already beginning her porridge.

'Goo' mornin',' she said politely. 'Did you hear me cleanin' my teef?'

He crushed her with a glance.

He sat eating in silence till everyone had come down and Aunts Jane, Evangeline and Lucy were consuming porridge with that mixture of festivity and solemnity that they felt the occasion demanded.

Then Jimmy entered, radiant, with a tin in his hand.

'Got presents,' he said proudly. 'Got presents, lots of presents.'

He deposited on Barbara's plate a worm which Barbara promptly threw in his face. Jimmy looked at her reproachfully and proceeded to Aunt Evangeline. Aunt Evangeline's gift was a centipede – a live centipede which ran off the tablecloth on to Aunt Evangeline's lap before anyone could stop it. With a yell that sent William's father from the room with his hands to his ears, Aunt Evangeline leapt onto her chair and stood with her skirts held to her knees.

'Help! Help!' she cried. 'The horrible boy! Catch it! Kill it!'

Jimmy gazed at her in amazement, and Barbara looked with interest at Aunt Evangeline's long expanse of shin.

'*My* legs isn't like *your* legs,' she said pleasantly and conversationally. 'My legs is knees.'

It was some time before order was restored, the centipede killed, and Jimmy's remaining gifts thrown out of the window. William looked across the table at Jimmy with respect in his eye . . . Jimmy was eating porridge unconcernedly . . .

'How was I to know she didn't like insecks?' he said aggrievedly. 'I like 'em.'

Richmal Crompton
(from 'More William')

47

A BABY FOR CHRISTMAS

(Cross, unhappy Angelica Cobb, who is not looking forward at all to having a new baby brother, is outside the hospital when she meets the ward Sister.)

'You'd better come inside and see them,' Sister said. Angelica followed her through the swing doors and along the shining corridor. 'I thought I wasn't allowed in?' she said.

'It's Christmas,' said Sister, going through another swing door. 'Everything's different at Christmas.'

Angelica found herself in a small ward. There were cots all round. Twelve cots. And a baby in every cot . . . And every baby was wearing a plastic bracelet with its name on.

'Which is my baby?' Angelica said.

'Look at the bracelets,' Sister said, bustling away between the cots. 'I've got things to do.' . . .

Angelica walked slowly along looking at the names. 'Christopher Cobb, this is our baby,' she said, looking at the wrist sticking out of the white bundle. She looked at the baby then, his face was wrinkled and purple-red, like the new skin when you picked a scab, Angelica thought. Christopher Cobb had new skin all over. He wasn't beautiful, he wasn't as beautiful as her baby doll for instance. He didn't have shining blue eyes and he didn't have any eyelashes at all. 'Hallo,' Angelica whispered.

'Come along now,' Sister said.

'He smiled at me,' Angelica said and there was a funny feeling in the back of her throat.

'That's wind,' said Sister. 'Off you go now.'

A lady in a red dressing-gown came through the door. It was Mummy. 'Angelica?' she said. 'How on earth did you get here?'

'I just walked,' said Angelica and then she flung her arms round her mother and buried her face in the red dressing-gown. 'He smiled at me,' Angelica said, sniffing rather.

Geraldine Kaye
(from 'A Different Sort of Christmas')

THAT THING ON THE TREE

At the end of the party, when our mothers came to take us home, they said we could all have a present off the Christmas tree. They said I could choose first because I was the smallest.

I said I wanted that thing on top of the tree, that shiny thing. I'd been looking at it all through the party, all through the hard white coconut cake that had taken me all teatime to eat; all through the games that I didn't know how to play; and all through the funny man with the cardboard nose who'd made me cry. I said I wanted that thing on top of the tree, that shiny thing.

Ah no, they said, I didn't want that. It wasn't a present. It was just to make the tree look pretty. Wouldn't I like this grand blue motor-car filled with sweets?

I said I wanted that thing on top of the tree, that shiny thing.

But I wouldn't be able to play with it or anything, they said. It was made of very thin stuff that broke as soon as you touched it. Wouldn't I like these pretty pink beads to put round my neck?

I said I wanted that thing on top of the Christmas tree. That shiny thing.

But what would I do with it, they said. Now what about these nice red gloves to keep my hands warm on cold days? What would I do with that thing on top of the tree?

I said I'd keep it in a cardboard box and look at it.

Then someone said, oh, give it her. When it's broke she'll be sorry she didn't have the blue car or the pink beads or the red gloves. So they put the shiny thing in a box and I carried it home and I looked at it. It was like having a star in a box, a star all of my own. Next day I lifted the thing out of the box and it broke into a thousand pieces. But every piece was shiny so I put them all back in the box again. And now I had a whole boxful of stars.

That was forty years ago, but some people never learn. Every time they ask me to choose I say I want that thing on top of the tree, that shiny thing.

So I've never had a grand blue motor-car or pretty pink beads to put round my neck or nice red gloves to keep my hands warm on cold days.

But I've got hundreds of thousands of cardboard boxes. And every box is full of a thousand stars.

Stella Johns

49

THE REAL MEANING

Christmas is a time to share happiness;
to give presents,
to laugh and joke together,
to thank God for everything.

We rejoice with Christians all over the world.
We rejoice with children of other lands:
children of many colours
and ways of life.
May the peace and blessings of the Christ Child
be for all children;
May we grow in the way of Jesus;
and know the real meaning of Christmas.

Anon.

CHRISTMAS PRAYER

O God, our loving Father,
help us rightly to remember the birth of Jesus,
that we may share in the song of the angels,
the gladness of the shepherds
and the worship of the wise men . . .

May the Christmas morning make us happy
to be thy children
and the Christmas evening bring us to our beds
with grateful thoughts,
forgiving and forgiven, for Jesus' sake.

Amen.

Robert Louis Stevenson

The Goodwill Runs Out

THE NEED TO BE NASTY

Do you know that time, towards the end of Christmas Day, when the goodwill sometimes runs out? Exhausted parents flop in their chairs among the debris; children, bloated but cheerful, play with their new possessions on the rug; and then, all of a sudden, all hell breaks loose. Children start to fight, there are tears and tantrums, someone's new toy gets broken and it will be surprising if parents don't lose their tempers too – with each other and the children.

The goodwill has run out. It has been a strain being kind and grateful and feeling that everything must be enjoyed. We can't keep up being nice any more; it's time to be nasty, to be ungrateful, unkind. Adult or child, we probably feel we hate our rotten family, and if not on Christmas Day, then certainly we feel it sometime.

I think this is one of the best things about families – that you can hate them, one at a time or the whole lot at once. You can be nasty, really nasty, and they will still be around tomorrow when you love them.

Patrick Parry Okeden

THE WORM TURNS

(Professor Peter Shandy, who teaches at an American college, feels that his neighbours overdo their Christmas decorations)

With a finesse born of much practice, Professor Shandy backed Mrs Ames off his front step and shut the door. This was the seventy-third time in eighteen years she'd nagged him about decorating his house. The tradition dated back, as Professor Shandy had taken the trouble to find out, no farther than 1931, when the wife of the then president (of the college) . . . had found a box of Japanese lanterns . . . and decided to stage a Grand Illumination on Christmas Eve. The Grand Illumination . . . had been such a smashing success that the college had repeated the event every year since . . . From near and far came tourists to bask in the spectacle . . . Pictures appeared in national magazines. However, the photographers always had to shoot one dark spot on the gala scene. This was the home of Peter Shandy . . .

Left to himself, Peter Shandy would willingly have made some concession to the event: a balsam wreath or a spray of holly on the front door, and a fat white candle guttering in the parlour window after dark. He rather liked Christmas. But altogether too many of Shandy's Christmases had been blighted by the overwhelmingly Christmas spirit around the Crescent. On this morning of December 21 . . . something snapped.

On the morning of December 22, two men drove up to the brick house in a large truck. The professor met them at the door.

'Did you bring everything, gentlemen?'

'The whole works. Boy, you folks up here sure take Christmas to heart!'

'We have a tradition to maintain,' said Shandy. 'You may as well start on the spruce trees.'

All morning the workmen toiled. Expressions of amazed delight appeared on the faces of neighbours and students. As the day wore on and the men kept at it, the amazement remained but the delight faded.

It was dark before the men got through. Peter Shandy walked them out to the truck. He was wearing his overcoat, hat and galoshes, and carrying a case.

'Everything in good order, gentlemen? Lights timed to flash on and off at six-second intervals? Amplifiers turned up to full volume? Steel-cased switch boxes provided with sturdy locks? Very well, then, let's flip on the power and be off . . .'

Precisely forty-eight hours later, on Christmas Eve, Professor Shandy stepped outside for a breath of air. Around him rolled the vast Atlantic. Above shone only the freighter's riding lights and a skyful of stars. The captain's dinner had been most enjoyable.

Back on the Crescent, floodlights would be illuminating the eight life-size reindeer mounted on the roof of the brick house. In its windows, sixteen Santa Claus faces would be leering above sixteen sets of artificial candles, each containing three red and two purple bulbs, each window outlined by a border of thirty-six more bulbs alternating in green, orange and blue.

He glanced at his watch and did rapid calculations in his head. At that precise point, the 742 outsize red bulbs on the spruce trees would have flashed on for the 28,800th time. The amplifiers must by now have blared out 2,536 renditions of 'I'm Dreaming of a White Christmas', 'I Saw Mommy Kissing Santa Claus' and 'All I Want For Christmas Is My Two Front Teeth'. They must be just now on the seventeenth bar of the 2,537th playing of 'I Don't Care Who You Are, Fatty, Get Those Reindeer Off My Roof'.

Professor Shandy smiled into the darkness. 'Bah, humbug,' he murmured, and began to count the stars.

Charlotte MacLeod   *53*
(from 'Rest You Merry')

FRIENDS AND RELATIONS

(Pip, a Victorian orphan boy, has been brought up by his bad-tempered sister, who is married to the kindly Joe. He is not looking forward to his Christmas dinner.)

Mr Wopsle was to dine with us; and Mr Hubble, the wheelwright, and Mrs Hubble; and Uncle Pumblechook, who was a well-to-do corn-chandler in the nearest town.

Among this company I felt myself in a false position. Not because I was squeezed in at an acute angle of the tablecloth, with the table in my chest and the Pumblechookian elbow in my eye, nor because I was not allowed to speak (I didn't want to speak), nor because I was given the scaly tips of the drumsticks of the fowls and with those obscure corners of pork of which the pig, when living, had had the least reason to be vain. No, I should not have minded that, if they would only have left me alone. But they wouldn't leave me alone. They seemed to think the opportunity lost, if they failed to point the conversation at me, every now and then, and stick the point into me.

It began the moment we sat down to dinner. Mr Wopsle said grace, and ended with the very proper wish that we might be truly grateful. Upon which my sister fixed me with her eye, and said, in a low, reproachful voice, 'Do you hear that? Be grateful.'

'Especially,' said Mr Pumblechook, 'be grateful, boy, to them which brought you up by hand.'

Mrs Hubble shook her head, and asked, 'Why is it that the young are never grateful?' This moral mystery seemed too much for the company until Mr Hubble solved it by saying, 'Naturally vicious.' Everybody then murmured, 'True!' and looked at me in a particularly unpleasant and personal manner.

Joe's influence was something feebler (if possible) when there was company, than when there was none. But he always aided and comforted me when he could, in some way of his own. There being plenty of gravy today, Joe spooned into my plate, at this point, about half a pint.

A little later in the dinner, Mr Wopsle remarked that he considered the subject of the morning's sermon ill-chosen, which was the less excusable, he added, when there were so many subjects 'going about'.

'True again,' said Uncle Pumblechook. 'Look at Pork alone. There's a subject!'

'True, sir. Many a moral for the young,' returned Mr Wopsle; and I knew he was going to lug me in, before he said it, 'might be drawn from that.'

('You listen to this,' said my sister to me, severely.)

Joe gave me some more gravy.

'Swine,' said Mr Wopsle, in his deepest voice and pointing his fork at my blushes as if he were mentioning my Christian name, 'Swine were the companions of the prodigal. The gluttony of Swine is put before us as an example to the young.' (I thought this pretty well in him who had been praising up the pork for being so plump and juicy.) 'What is detestable in a pig, is more detestable in a boy.'

'Or girl,' suggested Mr Hubble.

'Of course, or girl, Mr Hubble,' agreed Mr Wopsle rather irritably, 'but there is no girl present.'

Joe offered me some more gravy, which I was afraid to take.

Charles Dickens
(from 'Great Expectations', slightly adapted)

THE MYSTERY FADES

Gradually there gathered the feeling of expectation. Christmas was coming.
In the shed, at nights, a secret candle was burning, a sound of veiled voices was heard. The boys were learning the old mystery play of St George and Beelzebub. Twice a week, by lamplight, there was choir practice in the church, for the learning of old carols Brangwen wanted to hear. The girls went to these practices. Everywhere was a sense of mystery and rousedness. Everybody was preparing for something.

The time came near, the girls were decorating the church, with cold fingers binding holly and fir and yew about the pillars, till a new spirit was in the church, the stone broke out into dark, rich leaf, the arches put forth their buds, and cold flowers rose to blossom in the dim, mystic atmosphere. Ursula must weave mistletoe over the door, and over the screen, and hang a silver dove from a sprig of yew, till dusk came down, and the church was a grove.

In the cow-shed the boys were blacking their faces for a dress rehearsal; the turkey hung dead, with opened, speckled wings, in the dairy. The time was come to make pies, in readiness.

The expectation grew more tense. The star was risen into the sky, the songs, the carols were ready to hail it. The star was the sign in the sky. Earth too should give a sign. As evening drew on, hearts beat fast with anticipation, hands were full of ready gifts. There were the tremulously expectant words of the church service, the night was past and the morning was come, the gifts were given and received, joy and peace made a flapping of wings in each heart, there was a great burst of carols, the Peace of the World had dawned, strife had passed away, every hand was linked in hand, every heart was singing.

It was bitter, though, that Christmas day, as it drew on to evening and night, became a sort of bank holiday, flat and stale. The morning was so wonderful, but in the afternoon and the evening the ecstasy perished like a nipped thing, like a bud in false spring. Alas, that Christmas was only a domestic feast, a feast of sweetmeats and toys! Why did not the grown-ups also change their everyday hearts, and give way to ecstasy? Where was the ecstasy?

D.H. Lawrence
(from 'The Rainbow')

The Dark Side of the Road

UNDERNEATH THE ARCHES

The scene under the Railway Bridge was not what Alyce had anticipated . . . This evening – whether because it was Christmas or because despite the wind it was not a bitter night – the pavement on both sides of the road was crowded with figures, some lying flat, some sitting up with their backs to the wall as if in bed. In addition to these recumbent figures, other tramps were forming a loose queue at the rear of a white van parked against the kerb. On the side of the van were painted these words: 'Thanks be to God for His unspeakable gift'.

Despite the fact that the majority of tramps were sitting or lying down, the whole scene was given a sense of liveliness by the sound of the men calling to one another across the road like wounded soldiers in a vast, makeshift hospital ward. Between the shouts a harsh voice could be heard singing a tuneless and incoherent song. It was some time before Alyce located the source of this unattractive sound. She was amazed to see that the singer was a woman. It had not occurred to her that a woman could possibly be found among the flotsam of the city. Alyce watched her as she sang on undaunted by the curses of the men nearby. She did not look old but on the other hand she could not possibly be young: her hair was streaked yellow and grey and her face, which appeared to have swollen with some disease, was purple. With her right hand she grasped the neck of an empty bottle and held it tight against her side.

They walked forward, treading carefully between the feet of the men and the edge of the pavement. Few of the tramps were attempting to sleep, most preferring at this stage in the evening to chat to their neighbours or call across the street or just watch the comings and goings of the various mission vans and of the late night travellers from Charing Cross. Those men who were lying full length had obviously been at pains to keep out the cold. They were lying on one or two layers of thick cardboard (of which there appeared to be plentiful supply) and they had tied sheets of newspaper around each leg from the ankle to the knee. The feet had then been thrust into boxes and the boxes stuffed with paper. Though some of the men wore two overcoats and a few even had Balaclavas, the secret of sleeping rough was evidently to keep the feet warm at all costs.

John Rae
(from 'Christmas is Coming')

57

A PRISONER CAN UNDERSTAND

(In December 1943 Dietrich Bonhoeffer, a brilliant theologian and pastor of a church which had opposed Hitler, had been in a Nazi prison for nine months. He wrote to his parents:)

From the Christian point of view there is no special problem about Christmas in a prison cell. For many people in this building it will probably be a more sincere and genuine occasion than in places where nothing but the name is kept. That misery, suffering, poverty, loneliness, helplessness and guilt mean something quite different in the eyes of God from what they mean in the judgement of man, that God will approach where men turn away, that Christ was born in a stable because there was no room for him in the inn – these are things that a prisoner can understand better than other people; for him they really are glad tidings . . .

(Bonhoeffer wrote some prayers for the prisoners to use at Christmastime. This is an extract from his 'Morning Prayer')

O God, early in the morning I cry to you.
Help me to pray
And to concentrate my thoughts on you;
I cannot do this alone.

In me there is darkness,
But with you there is light;
I am lonely, but you do not leave me;
I am feeble in heart, but with you there is help;
I am restless, but with you there is peace.
In me there is bitterness, but with you there is patience;
I do not understand your ways,
But you know the way for me.

O heavenly Father,
I praise and thank you
For rest in the night;
I praise and thank you for this new day;
I praise and thank you for all your goodness
and faithfulness throughout my life.

You have granted me many blessings;
Now let me also accept what is hard
from your hand.
You will lay on me no more
than I can bear.
You make all things work together for good
for your children . . .

Give me such love for God and men
as will blot out all hatred and bitterness;
Give me the hope that will deliver me
from fear and faint-heartedness . . .
Lord, whatever this day may bring,
Your name be praised. Amen.

Dietrich Bonhoeffer

'. . . TO ALL OUR READERS'

(From the local weekly paper of a market-town in the south of England, one week before Christmas)

OLD FOLK FACE LONELY, DAMP, COLD CHRISTMAS

As thousands of families throughout Britain look forward to a traditional family celebration this Christmas, many old folk on a local council estate will be praying it will pass quickly.

One 85-year-old man has not a single heater in his house, and claimed he could not afford to light his coal fire.

Another pensioner said she would be spending Christmas Day alone, huddled in front of the gas fire – her only source of warmth. And others who have recently left hospital after suffering from chest complaints say they are terrified of spending winter in their damp houses.

But despite the catalogue of misery, the Council says there is just not enough money to provide central heating for these elderly residents.

One lady of 72 said: 'The doctor told me I should not go to bed in the bedroom as it is too cold, but sleep downstairs where the only fire is. There's black mould growing in the rest of the house and it has even started in here now. I will be on my own for Christmas Day, so I shall have to sit here by the fire.'

The chief housing officer for the Council pointed out: 'We have to look at the whole area, not just this estate. We have five other housing estates worse than this one.' He added that if there is a long hard winter, then money set aside for modernisation may be eaten away by mending burst pipes and so on. Eventually it boiled down to lack of money, he explained.

(In the centre of the front page, next to this story, was a large panel showing a beaming Father Christmas with the message: 'A Merry Christmas to All Our Readers.')

CHRISTMAS IN WAR-TIME

I heard the bells on Christmas day
Their old familiar carols play,
   And wild and sweet
   The words repeat
Of peace on earth, good-will to men!

And thought how, as the day had come,
the belfries of all Christendom
   Had rolled along
   The unbroken song
Of peace on earth, good-will to men!

Then from each black accursed mouth
The cannon thundered in the South,
   And with the sound
   The carols drowned
Of peace on earth, good-will to men!

It was as if an earthquake rent
The hearthstones of a continent,
   And made forlorn
   The households born
Of peace on earth, good-will to men!

And in despair I bowed my head;
'There is no peace on earth,' I said;
   'For hate is strong
   And mocks the song
Of peace on earth, good-will to men!'

Then pealed the bells more loud and deep;
'God is not dead; nor doth he sleep!
   The wrong shall fail,
   The right prevail,
With peace on earth, good-will to men!'

H.W. Longfellow

PRISON CAMP PUDDING, 1943

(In 1943 Ernest Gordon was a prisoner of the Japanese in the Far East, building the notorious bridge over the River Kwai.)

A Lancashire artillery captain welcomed us *(back to the hut after Christmas morning service in the camp church)* with the confidential air of one letting us in on a big secret.

'Back from your prayers, are you? Now that you've filled your souls you can fill your bellies. We're going to have a whopping dinner! Soup made from meat and bones! Rissoles with meat in them – rice and a slice of old Thai cow. And – to top it off – Christmas pudding!'

'Who're you kidding?' Bill and I chorused.

'You know the cook we've got in the kitchen?' the gunner said . . . 'The one who used to be some kind of technician in Blighty? The one who claims all you need to cook properly is intelligence?'

'Sure.'

'Well, he's invented Christmas pudding made from rice. First he boils it, see, then leaves it to ferment along with bananas, limes and palm sugar, then steams it. Wait till you taste it!'

We hurried to fetch our mess tins. We wanted to be sure to be in line at the serving-rack outside the hut when the dinner arrived to savour this miracle for ourselves.

It was the first decent meal we'd had in two years. The ration of meat was small by normal standards, but lavish by those of Chungkai. I ate slowly, enjoying every mouthful and the festive atmosphere. Then came the pudding. It was delicious. Not quite like anything I'd tasted before – but delicious . . .

Ernest Gordon
(from 'Miracle on the River Kwai')

STARVATION CHRISTMAS

(For three months a little township of eighty settlers on the American prairie, over a hundred years ago, has been cut off by blizzards from its only source of supplies: the railway. The town's two grocery shops are empty, and Laura's Christmas dinner is to be soup from two cans of oysters, the last food on the shelves, with the last milk from the family cow. But on Christmas Day the morning is sunny and they are expecting a train next day.)

At noon Ma was making oyster soup. Laura was setting the table, Carrie and Grace were playing with the jumping-jack. Ma tasted the soup and set the kettle back on the stove. 'The oysters are ready,' she said, and stooping she looked at the slices of bread toasting in the oven. 'And the bread is toasted. Whatever is Pa doing?'

'He's bringing in hay,' said Laura.

Pa opened the door. Behind him the lean-to was almost full of hay. He asked, 'Is the oyster soup ready?'

'I'm taking it up,' Ma replied. 'I'm glad the train is coming, this is the last of the coal.' Then she looked at Pa and asked 'What is wrong, Charles?'

Pa said slowly, 'There is a cloud in the north-west.'

'Oh, not another blizzard!' Ma cried.

'I'm afraid so,' Pa answered. 'But it needn't spoil our dinner.' He drew his chair up to the table. 'I've packed plenty of hay into the stable and filled the lean-to. Now for our oyster soup!'

The sun kept on shining while they ate. The hot soup was good, even though the milk was mostly water . . .

Laura enjoyed the good soup, but she could not stop thinking of that dark cloud coming up. She could not stop listening for the wind that she knew would soon come.

It came with a shriek. The windows rattled and the house shook.

'She must be a daisy!' Pa said. He went to the window but he could not see out. Snow came on the wind from the sky. Snow rose from the hard drifts as the wind cut them away. It all met in the whirling air and swirled madly. The sky, the sunshine, the town, were gone, lost in that blinding dance of snow. The house was alone again.

Laura thought, 'The train can't come now.'

'Come, girls,' Ma said, 'We'll get these dishes out of the way, and then we'll open our papers and have a cosy afternoon.'

'Is there coal enough, Ma?' Laura asked.

Pa looked at the fire. 'It will last till suppertime,' he said. 'And then we'll burn hay.'

Frost was freezing up the windowpanes and the room was cold near the walls.

For supper there were hot boiled potatoes and a slice of bread apiece, with salt. That was the last baking of bread, but there were still beans in the sack and a few turnips . . . While they were eating, the lamp began to flicker. With all its might the flame pulled itself up, drawing the last drops of kerosene up the wick. Then it fainted down and desperately tried again. Ma leaned over and blew it out. The dark came in, loud with the roar and the shrieking of the storm.

'The fire is dying, anyway, so we may as well go to bed.' Ma said gently. Christmas Day was over.

Laura Ingalls Wilder
(from 'The Long Winter')

NO ROOM

No room in the Holiday Inn;
No room in the holiday for them!
'Two hots and a cot' at the 'Army'
And a cardboard box
    over a sewer grate
    Is 'home' and a 'central heat'.

And they shall be called
    'shopping bag ladies',
    'street people',
    'the homeless'.

They know about
    giving birth on the run
    and keeping on the move
      to stay alive.
Smelly places of birth
    and lonely places of death
    are more than
      Bible stories to them.

They peer into the window
    of my soul:
    decorated as it is
    with Christmas lights
    and presents under the tree.
And I gaze out into the dark:
    the night in which
    an anonymous Joseph and Mary
    seek a place in my world
    for love to be born.

No room in the Holiday Inn;
    not even room in the holiday
    for love to be born. Alas!

Cornelius Kanhai

PRAYER FOR THE HOMELESS

Lord, who left the highest heaven
for a homeless human birth
and, a child within a stable,
came to share the life of earth –
    with your grace and mercy bless
    all who suffer homelessness.

Timothy Dudley-Smith

A LIGHT TO OTHERS

Dear Jesus, help us to spread your fragrance everywhere we go.
Flood our souls with your spirit and life.
Penetrate and possess our whole being so utterly that our
    lives may only be a radiance of yours.
Shine through us, and be so in us, that every soul we come
    in contact with may feel your presence in our soul.
Let them look up and see no longer us but only Jesus!
Stay with us, and then we shall begin to shine as you shine;
so to shine as to be a light to others; the light, O Jesus,
    will be all from you, none of it will be ours;
it will be you, shining on others through us.
Let us thus praise you in the way you love best by
    shining on those around us.
Let us preach you without preaching, not by words
    but by our example, by the catching force, the
    sympathetic influence of what we do,
the evident fullness of the love our hearts bear to you.
    Amen.

John Henry Newman

Where the Road Leads

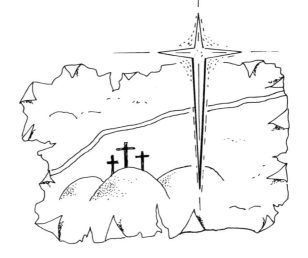

HERE WITH US

In the Christmas story
    Two things stand out clear:
People thought God far away,
    But they found him near.
Folk who took for granted
    Class and race divide,
There around the manger
    Knelt down side by side.

Still the rush-hour masses
    Assume you're far away;
Show us, Lord of everywhere,
    You're here with us today.
Still we think divided
    Bosses, leaders, men:
Lord, because we follow you
    Make us one again.

Lilian Cox

CHRISTMAS IS REALLY FOR THE CHILDREN

Christmas is really
for the children.
Especially for children
who like animals, stables,
stars and babies wrapped
in swaddling clothes.
Then there are wise men,
kings in fine robes,
humble shepherds and a
hint of rich perfume.

Easter is not really
for the children
unless accompanied by
a cream-filled egg.
It has whips, blood, nails,
a spear and allegations
of body snatching.
It involves politics, God
and the sins of the world.
It is not good for people
of a nervous disposition.
They would do better to
think on rabbits, chickens
and the first snowdrop of spring.

Or they'd do better to
wait for a re-run of
Christmas without asking
too many questions about
what Jesus did when he grew up
or whether there's any connection.

Steve Turner

THE SHEEP ON BLACKENING FIELDS

The sheep on blackening fields
No weather-warning know
As the thin, sapping sun
Annihilates the snow.
Winter has eased its grip,
The struck fountain flows;
Burns in its lamp of leaves
The white flame of the rose.

In the stiff river's gut
Fish and blurred stars unfreeze;
Unclench at the moor's side
The fists of trees.
Unscientifically housed
And in his hand a stone,
Grizzles in dusty hay
A naked child, alone.

A star of bitter red
Above the mountain crest
Writes on the squalling dark,
'Christus natus est.'
Silently we renew
The spoiled bread, the burned wine;
Take the huge-bellied child
Whose flesh is yours, is mine.

Charles Causley

CHRISTMAS NOW

Child, when Herod wakes,
and hate or exploitation
swing their dripping swords,
from your cross and cradle
    sing a new song.

    Child, when Caesar's laws
    choke love or strangle freedom,
    calling darkness light,
    from your cross and cradle
        sing a new song.

Child, when Caiaphas
sends truth to crucifixion
to protect his prayers,
from your cross and cradle
    sing a new song.

    Child, your helpless love
    brings death and resurrection:
    joyfully we come
    to your cross and cradle
        with a new song –
        Alleluia! Alleluia!

Brian Wren

CHRIST FROM HEAVEN'S GLORY COME

Christ from heaven's glory come,
in a stable make your home.
Helpless new-born babe-in-arms,
dream of terror's night-alarms.
Lullaby, my little love,
Herod's troops are on the move.

Cradled on a mother's knee,
immigrant and refugee,
talking, walking hand in hand,
homeless in a foreign land,
Child of Mary, full of grace,
exile of an alien race.

Christ whose hand the hungry fed,
stones were yours in place of bread;
Christ whose love our ransom paid,
by a kiss at last betrayed;
friendless now and nothing worth,
join the outcasts of the earth.

Soon the soldiers' jest is done,
'They will reverence my Son.'
On the gallows hang him high,
'By our law he ought to die.'
Perished, all the flower of youth:
Wash your hands, for what is truth?

Christ who once at Christmas came,
move our hearts who name your Name.
By your body, bring to birth
truth and justice, peace on earth,
sinners pardoned, love restored –
Reign among us, risen Lord!

Timothy Dudley-Smith

THE MARRIAGE CAROL

The marriage was made in winter
When Mary's son was born;
The marriage was made in April
When he was crowned with thorn.

Made it was in Nazareth,
And made in Bethlehem.
And made it was when Jesus rose,
In Jerusalem.

Married were we at Christmas,
And so may merry lie;
Married were we at Easter,
And so shall never die.

Jenny Overton

SING ROUND THE SEASONS

When from the sky in the splendour of summer
sunlight pours down over roof, over wood,
we sing of the kindness, extravagant kindness,
of God who is Father and Lord of all good.

When all around us the glory of autumn
colours the gardens, the fields and the hills,
we sing of the wonder, unspeakable wonder,
of God who with joy both begins and fulfils.

When in the coldness and deadness of winter
storms from the east with their bluster begin,
we sing of that morning, mysterious morning,
when Jesus was born in the barn of an inn.

When in the gladness and greenness of springtime
winter is over in life and in light,
we sing of that Easter, miraculous Easter,
that shattered the darkness and dread of the night.

Alan T. Dale 73

THE WORK OF CHRISTMAS

When the song of the angel is stilled,
When the star in the sky is gone,
When the Kings and the princes are home,
The work of Christmas begins.
> To find the lost
> To heal the broken
> To feed the hungry
> To release the prisoner
> To rebuild the nations
> To bring peace among brothers
> To make music in the heart.

Anon.

FATHER OF ALL

God is not far away;
he is not out of reach.
He, who existed before the universe,
who created
and has power over all things,
is here,
in our worship.
He is not brown or black or white;
he is the Father of all
and through him we live.

He is with us in all the confusion
of modern life.
He comes to us in Jesus Christ,
to live among us;
to make himself known to us,
yesterday,
today,
and tomorrow.

Anon.

THANKSGIVING

Therefore with all angels and archangels
And tongues of computers
We give thanks to the romping God
Who through impossibility
Hath delivered us
Into the madness and gladness
Of sure knowledge and salvation

Chad Walsh

PLEASE LOOK

(From a letter written by a poor monk, Fra Giovanni, to the Contessina Allagia della Aldobrandeschi, a great Italian lady, on Christmas Eve, 1513.)

There is nothing I can give you which you have not got; but there is much, very much, that, while I cannot give it, you can take. No heaven can come to us unless our hearts find rest in it today.
Take heaven! No peace lies in the future which is not hidden in this present little instance. Take peace! The gloom of the world is but a shadow. Behind it, yet within reach, is joy. There is radiance and glory in the darkness, could we but see – and to see we have only to look.
I beseech you to look.

LIFE STORY

Sing my song backwards, from end to beginning,
    Friday to Monday, from dying to birth.
Nothing is altered, but hope changes everything:
    sing Resurrection and peace upon earth!

Whisper a hope through the shame and agony,
    horror and emptiness darker than night,
wounds of Golgotha and hell of Gethsemane –
    weep Resurrection and clothe them in light!

Gather the sinews and dry bones of memory –
    healings and parables, laughter and strife,
joy with the outcasts and love for the enemy –
    breathe Resurrection and dance them to life!

Stretch out a rainbow from cross to nativity.
    Deck out the stable with shepherds and kings,
angels and miracles, glory and poetry:
    sing my song backwards till all the world sings!

Brian Wren

Sources and Acknowledgements

The editor and publishers gratefully acknowledge permission to reproduce the following copyright material:

Weather for the Road
LEGENDARY WINTER T.H. White: from *The Sword in the Stone* (Collins).
ONLY SNOW Allan Ahlberg: from *Please Mrs Butler* (Puffin), reprinted by permission of Penguin Books Ltd.
A PRAYER BEFORE CHRISTMAS IN A TOWN Chris Herbert.

A Time of Waiting
'BE IT UNTO ME . . .' Kathleen Raine: from *Collected Poems*, reprinted by permission of George Allen and Unwin Ltd.
ADVENT PRAYERS Michael Walker: from *Everyday Prayers* (NCEC)
ADVENT CAROLS Jenny Overton: from *The Thirteen Days of Christmas* (Puffin), reprinted by permission of Faber and Faber Ltd.

Coming to the Stable
THE SAFETY OF THE WORLD Mary Coleridge.
'O SIMPLICITAS' Madeleine L'Engle: from *The Weather of the Heart*, reprinted by permission of Harold Shaw Publishers.
LITTLE-BORN JESUS from *Children in Search of Meaning* by Violet Madge (SCM Press).
THE END OF A JOURNEY Alan Garner: from *Holly from the Bongs*, by Alan Garner and Roger Hill (Collins).
JESUS AS GOD THE SON Dorothy L. Sayers: from *The Zeal of Thy House* (Gollancz), reprinted by permission of David Higham Associates Ltd.
THE HOUSE OF CHRISTMAS G.K. Chesterton: from *The Wild Knight*, (J.M. Dent, 1935).
THE NORTH SHIP: LEGEND Philip Larkin: from *Collected Poems*, reprinted by permission of Faber and Faber Ltd.
THE WORD WAS IN DARKNESS Sister Mary Oswin: from *Let God's Children Sing* (Geoffrey Chapman).
THE LORD OF LIGHT from the Greek Orthodox Christmas Vigil Service, in *The Festal Manaion*, translated by Mother Mary and Kallistos Ware, reprinted by permission of Faber and Faber Ltd.
HUSH YOU, MY BABY Timothy Dudley-Smith: (verses 1 and 5) from *Lift Every Heart* (Collins).
NONE TOO POOR Rita Snowden: from *While the Candle Burns* (Epworth Press).
THE BETHLEHEM STAR Gerard Manley Hopkins.

Christmas Companions
THE WITNESSES Joyce Goldmanis: from *Together* magazine.
SPANISH CAROL Ruth Sawyer: from *The Long Christmas* (The Bodley Head Ltd).
CAROL OF THE ANIMALS Sister Maris Stella: from *Frost for St Bridget* (Sheed and Ward, 1949).
CAROL FOR THE DOG Sister Maris Stella: from *Frost for St Bridget* (Sheed and Ward, 1949).
ROBIN'S ROUND U.A. Fanthorpe: from *Standing To* (Harry Chambers/Peterloo Poets, Treovis Farm Cottage, Upton Cross, Liskeard, Cornwall).

Yesterdays
NO CHRISTMAS, BY ORDER: 1657 John Evelyn: from his *Diary*.
ELIZABETHAN MANOR-HOUSE CHRISTMAS Alison Uttley: from *A Traveller in Time*, reprinted be permission of Faber and Faber Ltd.
THE ACCURSED THING Edmund Gosse: from *Father and Son* (1907).
A LONDON CHRISTMAS IN THE 1870s Molly V. Hughes: from *A London Child of the 1870s* (Oxford University Press).
TWO SIDES OF THE DAY Elizabeth Goudge: from *The Dean's Watch* (Hodder and Stoughton).
CHRISTMAS SIGHTS AND SOUNDS Alison Uttley: from *The Country Child*, reprinted by permission of Faber and Faber Ltd.
THE CAROL SINGERS Alison Uttley: from *The Country Child*, reprinted by permission of Faber and Faber Ltd.

Here and Now

WELLS CATHEDRAL AT CHRISTMAS Michael O'Higgins: from *Wells and Other Poems* (Arthur H. Stockwell Ltd).
MOMENT OF TENSION David Lankshear.
CAROL SINGERS Geoff Terry: from *The Crib and the Cross* (The Book Guild, 25 High Street, Lewes, Sussex).
THE BABY HAD A BIRTHDAY Cecily Taylor: from *Contract* (Galliard/Stainer and Bell), reprinted by permission of the author.
'. . . AND A PARTRIDGE IN A PEAR TREE' Jenny Overton: from *The Thirteen Days of Christmas*, (Puffin) reprinted by permission of Faber and Faber Ltd.
THE HERDMANS AND THE NATIVITY PLAY Barbara Robinson: from *The Worst Kids in the World*, reprinted by permission of Faber and Faber Ltd. (Also published as *The Best Christmas Pageant Ever*).
WILLIAM GIVES PRESENTS Richmal Crompton: from *More William* (Macmillan).
JIMMY GIVES PRESENTS TOO Richmal Crompton: from *More William* (Macmillan).
A BABY FOR CHRISTMAS Geraldine Kaye: from *A Different Sort of Christmas* (Kaye and Ward).
THAT THING ON THE TREE Stella Johns: from BBC radio programme 'Northern Drift', included in *Living Expressions* (Ginn), reprinted by permission of Ginn and Co. Ltd.
THE REAL MEANING Anon.
CHRISTMAS PRAYER Robert Louis Stevenson.

The Goodwill Runs Out

THE NEED TO BE NASTY Patrick Parry Okeden: from *Pause for Thought on Radio 2* (BBC Publications 1971), reprinted by permission of the author.
THE WORM TURNS Charlotte Macleod: from *Rest You Merry* (Collins).
FRIENDS AND RELATIONS Charles Dickens: *Great Expectations*.
THE MYSTERY FADES D.H. Lawrence: *The Rainbow*, reprinted by permission of Laurence Pollinger Ltd. and the Estate of Mrs Frieda Lawrence Ravagli.

The Dark Side of the Road

UNDERNEATH THE ARCHES John Rae: from *Christmas is Coming* (Hodder and Stoughton), reprinted by permission of A.D. Peters & Co.
A PRISONER CAN UNDERSTAND Dietrich Bonhoeffer: from *Letters and Papers from Prison* (SCM Press).
'. . . TO ALL OUR READERS' A genuine extract from a weekly newspaper.
CHRISTMAS IN WARTIME Henry Wadsworth Longfellow.
PRISON CAMP PUDDING, 1943 Ernest Gordon: from *Miracle on the River Kwai* (Collins).
STARVATION CHRISTMAS Laura Ingalls Wilder: from *The Long Winter* (Puffin), reprinted by permission of James Clarke & Co.
NO ROOM Cornelius Kanhai: from *The Plough*, magazine of Woodcrest Bruderhof, New York State, USA, issue of December 1985.
PRAYER FOR THE HOMELESS Timothy Dudley-Smith: verse 1 of 'Lord, who left the highest heaven', from *Lift Every Heart* (Collins).
A LIGHT TO OTHERS John Henry Newman.

Where the Road Leads

HERE WITH US Lilian Cox: from *Christmas Candles* (NCEC).
CHRISTMAS IS REALLY FOR THE CHILDREN Steve Turner: from *Up to Date* (Hodder and Stoughton).
THE SHEEP ON BLACKENING FIELDS Charles Causley: from *Collected Poems 1951–1975* (Macmillan).
CHRISTMAS NOW Brian Wren: from *Mainly Hymns* (John Paul The Preacher's Press), reprinted by permission of Oxford University Press.
CHRIST FROM HEAVEN'S GLORY COME Timothy Dudley-Smith: from *Lift Every Heart* (Collins).
THE MARRIAGE CAROL Jenny Overton: from *The Thirteen Days of Christmas* (Puffin), reprinted by permission of Faber and Faber Ltd.
SING ROUND THE SEASONS Alan T. Dale: from *Gesture to Galilee* (privately printed).
THE WORK OF CHRISTMAS Anon.
FATHER OF ALL Anon.
THANKSGIVING Chad Walsh: included in *Rejoice!* (Muller).
PLEASE LOOK Fra Giovanni, 1513.
LIFE STORY Brian Wren: from *Mainly Hymns* (John Paul The Preacher's Press), reprinted by permission of Oxford University Press.